U. Gall Y4/Y5.

Escapades From The West Midlands

Edited By Machaela Gavaghan

First published in Great Britain in 2018 by:

 Young**Writers**

Young Writers
Remus House
Coltsfoot Drive
Peterborough
PE2 9BF
Telephone: 01733 890066
Website: www.youngwriters.co.uk

FOREWORD

Young Writers was created in 1991 with the express purpose of promoting and encouraging creative writing. Each competition we create is tailored to the relevant age group, hopefully giving each child the inspiration and incentive to create their own piece of work, whether it's a poem or a short story. We truly believe that seeing their work in print gives pupils a sense of achievement and pride in their work and themselves.

Every day children bring their toys to life, creating fantastic worlds and exciting adventures, using nothing more than the power of their imagination. What better subject then for primary school pupils to write about, capturing these ideas in a mini saga – a story of just 100 words. With so few words to work with, these young writers have really had to consider their words carefully, honing their writing skills so that every word counts towards creating a complete story.

Within these pages you will find stories about toys coming to life when we're not looking, the adventures they have with their owners and even a few tales of peril when toys go missing or get lost! Each one showcases the creativity and talent of these budding new writers as they learn the skills of writing, and we hope you are as entertained by them as we are.

CONTENTS

Finlay Moseley (10)   54
Sophie Markham (11)   55

Colwall CE Primary School, Colwall Green

Miriam Jarratt (11)   56
Alice Stocking (11)   57
Lucy Copeland (11)   58
Emily Glover (11)   59
Emonie Huckle (10)   60
Tilly Amy Davies (11)   61
Alysia Marriott (11)   62
Kombo Choma (11)   63
Lucy Isherwood (11)   64
Abi Knight (11)   65
Ben Friedlander (11)   66
Andy Smith (10)   67
Rowan Clark (11)   68
Yvaine Ragen Fraser (11)   69

Dixie Grammar School, Market Bosworth

George Zavalis (9)   70
Erin Brining (9)   71
Cian Geaghty (10)   72
Issy Parkes (10)   73
Imogen Green (9)   74
Ioan Daniel Hust-Edwards (9)   75
Oscar Harding (10)   76
Ava Constable (10)   77
Felicity Ava Dracup (10)   78

Fladbury CE (A) First School, Fladbury

Amelia Grace Parker (9)   79
Elsie Grace Morris (9)   80

Harper Bell SDA School, Birmingham

Zoe-Maria Palmer (11)   81

Hurley Primary School, Hurley

Isobel Cole (11)   82
Grace Thorpe (11)   83
Jack Samuel Freeman (11)   84
Jessica Jakovlevs (10)   85
Josh Matthew King (10)   86
Hope Olivia Williams (11)   87
George Knight (10)   88

Kempsey Primary School, Kempsey

Reuben Jenkins (9)   89
Jess Popham (9)   90
Millie Harris (9)   91
Bethany Hoskins (9)   92
Katie Cox (9)   93

Kilsby CE Primary School, Kilsby

Eloise Hardwick (9)   94
Layla Rose (8)   95
Joshua David Hurwood Fuentes (8)   96
Nicole Cloete (8)   97
Florence Stuart (7)   98

Kingsway Community Primary School, Leamington Spa

Diya Sharma (10)   99
Rohini Patil (11)   100

Kinlet CE Primary School, Bewdley

Jake Broome-Wright (9)   101
Jack Waterhouse-Turner (10)   102
Katie Ann Dudley (9)   103
Chloe Kinnersley (8)   104

Slade Primary School, Birmingham

Sarah Ishraq Garnier (8)	105
Robert Neill Barachina Fortuno (7)	106
Tanzeel Hussain (8)	107

St Anthony's Catholic Primary School, Kingshurst

Evan Rickard (9)	108
Oliwia Hebel (11)	109
Nariayah Webber (8)	110
Angel Sandhu (10)	111
Keontai Nathan Miley-Morgan (9)	112
Brooke Sims (9)	113
Darion Deathridge (10)	114

St Barnabas CE First & Middle School, Drakes Broughton

Alice Worley (11)	115
Beatrice Emilia Burrows (11)	116
Madison Amelia Tustin (11)	117

St Bede's Catholic Middle School, Redditch

Olivia Edwards (11)	118

The Croft Preparatory School, Stratford-Upon-Avon

Georgia Keyte (10)	119
Charlie Feaver (9)	120
Tim (10)	121
Nathaniel Joshi (10)	122
Theo Holland (9)	123
Daniel Nichols (10)	124
Georgia Eve Hay (10)	125
Alannah Swift (10)	126
Benji Thorne (10)	127
Olivia Phillis (10)	128

Beatrix Burman (10)	129
Thomas Russell (10)	130

The Willows CE Primary School, Stratford-Upon-Avon

Daniel James Beaman (9)	131
Isabella Mae Charles (8)	132
Ava Craddock (9)	133
Hannah Gascoyne-Davies (8)	134
Alfie Price (9)	135
Francesca Bannister (9)	136
Wiktor Czeszejko (9)	137
Matthew Hemming (8)	138
Sophie Olivia Hall (9)	139
Isaac Barnes (9)	140
Euan Clarke (8)	141
Cori-Annabel Tonia Byron (9)	142
Michael Green (9)	143
Oliver Hill (8)	144
Lily West (9)	145
James Hales (9)	146

THE MINI SAGAS

The Unforgiving Teddy Bear

The toy soldiers are marching after me. I'm the best tailor in the land, although I am known as the 'unforgiving teddy bear'. The king of toys trusted me to make a suit for his prestigious royal anniversary, but no one is cheeky enough to make me work for them. His troops must've already covered about two acres. I'm on the run, unable to steal love and tenderness. As most in this land, we're very fragile, and love is essential to life. Running into another dimension, I see a bed. I keep running until my owner hugs me for bedtime.

Abel Neto (11)

One Way Love

Boom! Boom! That's the sound of my heart beating when I look at Jeff. He's gorgeous. Look at that floppy hair and those big, brown eyes. Dreamy! He's way out of my league. As if he'd look at a thirty-centimetre rag doll like me! I'm wearing my prettiest frock but he still doesn't notice me. Then I wonder, *if I climb up onto my doll's house, he'll definitely see me.* I make my way onto the patterned roof as Jeff, just back from school, walks into the room. That's when I feel my foot start to slip...

Holly Carter (11)

King Max

While a little girl was sleeping, her toys were waking up from a long slumber. King Max strolled up and down the carpet while the stuffed animals were looking into the little girl's head to see her dreams. Max told the toys off if they had been naughty, like trying to change the girl's dream into a nightmare. He praised the toys that were good, like stopping the bad toys changing the dream. If you were really bad, you would get stuffed behind cupboards and you'd stay there until someone came looking for you, which didn't often happen.

Sophia May Thompson (9)

Lost

It was when Milly left Giraffe on the bus that the adventure started. Giraffe squeaked to her but no one heard. He went ignored for ages and everyone left one by one. Then a man holding a broom took him into an enormous building, full of everything imaginable! There was an atmosphere of waiting - for what Giraffe did not know.

One morning, who should come in? Milly! She had come at last for him! He saw her scanning the shelves and was terrified he wouldn't be seen! He gathered all his energy and *squeaked*! This time, she heard...

Seth B Fisher (10)

Molly And Sandra Hate Batteries

One by one, all the modern toys got sold, leaving Molly and Sandra. "I hate batteries," said Molly. "Me too," replied Sandra.

"Why don't they pick us? We don't need batteries, we have enough energy!" Molly said. In came two girls, laughing and giggling.

"Amina, that doll, it looks like you!"

"Aisha, that other doll also looks like you!" They picked up the dolls and cheered. "Dad, can we get these dolls? They never run out of energy, please!"

"Okay," grunted Dad, "you better play with them!"

So the dolls and the girls left with huge smiles!

Amina Nessa (11)
Al-Hijrah School, Bordesley Green

The Return Of Crysalis

One normal day, there lived three best friends, known as the 'main three' - Sweetie Pie, Rainbow Bright and Tricksy. They were having a sleepover because they'd defeated Queen Crysalis.

The next day, Queen Crysalis returned with a huge bullet-ant army. When the main three saw how big the army was, they thought they wouldn't be able to defeat an army so big. Rainbow Bright said, *"Teamwork makes the dream work!"* So, all together, the main three stood up to Queen Crysalis and defeated her. She was never seen again.

Always remember, friendship is magic and can conquer all things.

Zahra Sindhu (7)
Al-Hijrah School, Bordesley Green

Search Party

Angelina hears something and follows the sound. She gets lost in the woods. Raseena informs everyone that Angelina is lost. They search into the darkness of the night and extend their search in the creepy woodlands. Suddenly, Raseena hears a tiny voice. She calls for backup and follows the voice. As they go deeper into the woods, they face many scary situations. Fortunately, Ultra-Beeb is there to protect them. Eventually, they find Angelina and bring her home.
Just then, I feel a shudder. I open my eyes and look around. It was only a dream, what a relief!

Amirah Tahir (7)
Al-Hijrah School, Bordesley Green

The Ugly Potato Queen

Once upon a time, there was a queen who was a potato. She loved to look in the mirror and say, "Mirror, mirror, potatoes are the prettiest, only me!"

The magic mirror said, "Yes, you are the prettiest!" Then the queen went to the park. She then saw an ugly potato witch. The witch cast a spell so she swapped. The queen became the ugly witch and the witch turned pretty. The queen angrily wailed, "Help! I'm ugly!" No one cared, then she called the police. They were amazed that Her Majesty was ugly. The witch was arrested.

Amiira Yusuf (8)
Al-Hijrah School, Bordesley Green

The Girl Fairy!

A girl called Aimee once walked to school. She saw a shining light and followed it. It was a fairy! Aimee got a jar out of her old, tattered bag and trapped the fairy inside. She took the fairy to school but when she got there, the fairy had disappeared. But how? The jar was closed! Aimee and her friends looked everywhere but they still couldn't find the fairy. One of Aimee's friends, Emily, found a book of fairies and said, "A fairy dies by not having any air." So that afternoon, Aimee let the fairy go again.
"Woohoo!"

Hanaa Hussain (8)
Al-Hijrah School, Bordesley Green

The Evil Witch

One lovely day, a cute girl named Lily lived in a cottage.

The next day, she went for a good walk in the woods, then she saw some candy leading her to a strange place. She took all the candy until she reached Candy World. She screamed, "Mum! Dad! Help! I see a witch. Jessica! Judy! Anyone, please help!"

"No darling, I'm a nice witch, but my sister is evil. You may come into the house," laughed the witch. "Look in this cage and stay in there forever!"

"I am so scared, please let me go!"

Inayah Ali (8)
Al-Hijrah School, Bordesley Green

The Haunted Teddy Bear

One stormy night, a big girl named Lucy was babysitting her two cousins. They were watching 'The Haunted Teddy Bear'. They got frightened so they ran upstairs and out onto the balcony. They lived in a flat, at the top. Lucy grabbed them by the shoulders and came down.

After a while of watching the news, they had to go to bed. At 12pm, Lucy rushed down into the kitchen to see what was going on. She saw a shadow looking up at her and it chased her into the streets. She made a turn, leaving the teddy squashed forever.

Zaynab Ali (10)
Al-Hijrah School, Bordesley Green

Unusual Animals!

One gloomy night, there was an old, nasty man. He had a dragon, a sheep and a dog. The old man didn't know that they did different and unusual things. The dragon could talk, the sheep could fly and the dog could walk like a human! The old man treated them horribly and nastily. The dragon was thinking of a frightening plan to kill the cruel, old man. Sheep and Dog soon joined in and used their special talents to defeat the man. The dog ran out of its cage. The man chased after him and Dragon and Sheep flew...

Aisha Farah (8)
Al-Hijrah School, Bordesley Green

The Broken Bunny

There was once a toy rabbit. In the beginning, he was very splendid. He was very bouncy, as a toy rabbit should be, for at least two hours. The girl loved him. Then her friends came for a party. A girl said, "Can I play with your bunny?"
The girl said, "No!" She snatched the bunny, it snapped! Her auntie could fix anything. She gave it to her auntie. She couldn't fix it. The girl started to cry, then her auntie bought her a new one. She was very happy.

Maryam Mohamed (8)
Al-Hijrah School, Bordesley Green

The Magic Powers

Three thousand years ago in a magic castle, there lived a beautiful girl called Olivia. She was a princess. She had a mother who died. A wizard had always wanted her powers. He lived in a dark cave. One day, he came to the castle. He was as sneaky as a snake. He captured the princess and took her powers away. Then suddenly, a prince came for her. He killed the wizard and he hugged the princess. She got her powers back so she got married. They lived happily ever after.

Khadijha Muhroof (8)
Al-Hijrah School, Bordesley Green

My Little Teddy

Once upon a time, there lived a little teddy called Snuggles and he was in a shop, waiting for somebody to pick him up and take him home. Then, I bought him and I took him home and played with him. He was so cute and I used to take him everywhere with me. He was the best teddy I'd ever had. I always wanted to go back there again. I lived so happily that everyone was cheering for me. I loved it!

Aaisha Aamir (8)
Al-Hijrah School, Bordesley Green

Angel's Sweet Cafe

Barbie, Chelsea and Angel were busy in their cafe. All the toys came from miles to eat the delicious cakes. The Twirlywoos' boat parked outside Angel's cafe and out popped Great Big Who and Chick. They walked in and joined the queue. Chick was so excited about eating the cakes, he started counting them. "Oh no!" cried Chick. "There's only one left!" Luckily, Angel had an idea.

"Why don't you play a game of magnetic darts and the winner's prize is the last cake?"

"Yay, what a fantastic idea!"

"Let's play together!" Everyone was really, really happy.

Saffiyah Ali (8)
Birmingham Muslim School, Birmingham

A Chipmunk's Stoplight

Tick-tock, tick-tock. It'd been years since someone bought him, or at least, what it seemed like to Alvin. He had missed all the good times with his brothers, it almost seemed like they'd never happened. A new home was calling out for him somewhere, he just didn't know where. However, Alvin had at least found a plan that a normal chipmunk would never think of. A word popped into his head: 'Poster'. "Eureka! that's it!" he shrieked. Everyone turned towards him, then convinced themselves they were dreaming. It was hard being in the spotlight when you were a toy!

Nousayba Gaini (10)
Birmingham Muslim School, Birmingham

The Pirates' Escape

"Hurry! The coast is clear!" shouted one of the pirates.
"We can set sail as fast as we can!" cried another. With the human not there with them, the pirates began sailing silently and fast at the same time. It was their only chance to leave. They heard a hum. "Faster!" shouted one. "It's coming!" There was a loud splash as a bar of soap hit the ship. A big shape loomed over, Sally laughed when she saw her brother's pirate toys.
"How on earth did they get in the bath?" The pirates had to escape another time...

Shamila Islam (11)
Birmingham Muslim School, Birmingham

The Three-Faced Agent

"All agents to HQ, immediately!"
"There's reason to believe that Kachinggott's bank is safe and sound!" There was one massive round of applause from all spies. Congrats were said. Catflyosaurus was the trustworthy one. Cas was being informed of his mission. As a dinosaur, he waited until night. The trouble began as he flew, snoozing away. The bank was being attacked and nobody knew! They got away with it a couple of times but someone noticed. It was his last chance. "Where is the stadium?" Was his job in jeopardy?

Rumaysah Fadl-Elahi (11)
Birmingham Muslim School, Birmingham

The Three Puppies And The Fearsome Darkness

Once upon a time, there were three toys named Fifi, Riri and Titi. They had a dream and it was to become musketeers. They were courageous, brave and heroic.

One day, the city was overtaken by extreme weather so the puppies were the only ones to be courageous. They went further and further and they realised that they'd entered the darkness. Suddenly, they found an enormous diamond, which was as shiny as gold, so they took it and brought it to the city. The king said they were the bravest, most courageous musketeers that he'd ever seen!

Ayyoub Debeule (10)
Birmingham Muslim School, Birmingham

The Shape-Shifter

One stormy night, there lived a robot named Johnny and Johnny was an independent robot. He liked living independently. That was when he saw his neighbour coming out of his house. He came into the room and jumped onto the shelf. He shape-shifted into the robot that Johnny looked like. Johnny squealed, "Shape-shifter!" The shape-shifter turned its head and chanted a spell but the spell didn't work so he opened his metal and pulled out his spell book. He held his necklace and chanted once again. Johnny was never seen ever again.

Rumaysah Tahari (9)
Birmingham Muslim School, Birmingham

My Little Pony

Once upon a time, there were lots of ponies. All of them were happy to see the princess all day long and all of the time. All of the ponies were finding treasure. Rainbow Dash was very fast at flying. They set off on their journey.

They reached the cave of treasures. They saw a dragon sleeping in the cave. They tiptoed and grabbed the treasure out of the cave. The dragon didn't wake up. They flew back to the castle happily with the treasure. They saw Princess Luna on a chair and talked to her. They lived happily.

Aaisha Hussain (8)
Birmingham Muslim School, Birmingham

The Mysterious Princess

One day, as the mysterious princess woke up, she was gifted by her sister with a heart box with lots of lovely petals, but the mysterious princess never knew that they were magic.

Finally, it was night, but the mysterious princess was very hungry so she went to eat. All of a sudden, she heard footsteps coming towards the kitchen. It was her sister. Her sister made a dress out of the petals. The princess touched the palace and it turned to gold! She was amazed by this mysterious power from the petals!

Sidra Mirza (8)
Birmingham Muslim School, Birmingham

A Fashion Disaster

It was a good day or at least, what Lippy thought. She started by putting on her favourite perfume and tying her hair neatly into a bun. She looked very fashionable. Suddenly and out of nowhere, Cheeky Chocolate attacked her and smudged his chocolate on her. "Boo! I scared you!" Lippy couldn't believe how cheeky and naughty he was! "This is a total fashion disaster!" Straight away, she took her lipstick and literally covered him with it. It always felt good to get revenge!

Oumayma Gaini (8)
Birmingham Muslim School, Birmingham

Mimi

I was alone, living in garbage. No one liked me. It was like I was dead. Where would I go?

In the morning, a little girl was skipping. She saw me. She felt sorry for me and she picked me up and went to her mum and asked if she could keep me. Her mum allowed her to. I felt like I was finally going to be with someone forever.

After three weeks, the little girl gave me a name, which was so beautiful. It was Mimi.

After days, I became one of the best toys, living happily.

Rim Yassir (11)
Birmingham Muslim School, Birmingham

The Dragon

Once upon a time in a small city, it was a beautiful, very beautiful, city. It was full of flowers but there was great sadness in the day. They should've been giving the dragon one cow but all the farmers had finished. Because they were giving them to the dragon every day, all the cows had been eaten! The people went to see the king and they told him, "All our farmers have finished and the cows are finished." The king chose a girl to go into the home of the dragon...

Ismail Grellier (8)
Birmingham Muslim School, Birmingham

I Lost My Toy

I looked under my bed, he wasn't there. I had to hurry because I was bringing him to school to scare the bullies. What was I going to do? They were going to be waiting for me outside! As I walked, I felt scared. I had no one to help me. But then, I saw green hair spiking up behind the bush and I had some hope it was my monster. All of a sudden, the bush rustled and he jumped out in front of the bullies and roared! I hugged him tightly and we laughed.

Raiyaan Gibbs (8)
Birmingham Muslim School, Birmingham

The Lost Toy

In the morning, there was a girl playing with a toy. When it was night-time, she went to sleep. All the toys woke up! But there was only one big, giant toy. He was so scary. The others were good. There was a little, nice toy, he was so brave.
The mean toy pushed the nice toy into the window, then the nice toy went into the river! The river was so black that no one would ever go to it. The nice toy was still alive, then he went back home.

Maryem Yassir (9)
Birmingham Muslim School, Birmingham

The Army Men's Revenge!

It all started when the small, green army men tried to take Mia's attention. Mia, a kind and sensible girl, already had a favourite toy - Sparkle the unicorn! When Sparkle heard mumbling, she untucked herself from Mia's arm and found three, green men on Mia's desk. "What are you doing? It's midnight!" she asked, confused. There was no answer.

"Getting rid of you!" they finally said.

"Please don't because..." her voice was cut off by Mia.

"W-w-w-what? Come on Sparkle!" She pulled her rainbow, fluffy unicorn towards her in bed. Those nasty, green, army men were never seen again!

Ella Moore (10)
Chaddesley Corbett Endowed Primary School, Lower Chaddesley

The Talking Toy Unicorn

Once upon a time, there was a magical, talking unicorn who pranced off a little girl's shelf and the little girl recognised that she was singing a beautiful song called 'Photograph' to her handsome, charming, unicorn boyfriend. As quick as a flash, the talking unicorn jumped on her boyfriend's back and galloped to the window to jump out of the window next to the little girl's bed. Suddenly, the talking unicorn said, "Ahhh! This is fun!" But her precious boyfriend's leg collapsed, then a prince unicorn came to save the talking unicorn's boyfriend and took him to his doctor.

Charlotte Flint (8), Lottie Horne (7) & Hollie
Chaddesley Corbett Endowed Primary School, Lower Chaddesley

Lily's Life

A long time ago, Lily Leopard and her friend Scarlet Snake escaped their boxes, parked their magic set and made an evil spell. As Lily pulled out her pink dust, all the toys would fall into a deep sleep, but it backfired and broke Lily's leg. "Oh no!" screamed Lily as she held her leg in pain. Her friend Dave Dog fell asleep. Soon, Lily's leg was better and they flew off to New York, then they found their mums.
"Mum! Mum!" they shouted. They all lived happily ever after and were never mean again.

Jolea Farley (9)
Chaddesley Corbett Endowed Primary School, Lower Chaddesley

The Garden Escape

"The coast is clear Sergeant, everyone is ready for the escape and the monkey chains are waiting by the window."

"Okay, lower them down," said the sergeant. One by one, the chain of monkeys grew bigger and bigger.

"They've reached the floor Sergeant."

"Good, it's time to climb down. We've nearly escaped." The soldiers climbed down lower and lower until they reached the floor. "Everybody here?"

"Yes," replied the soldiers. Slowly, the soldiers edged along the wall until they reached the front garden.

"We've nearly escaped!" one soldier shouted. Suddenly, a dark shadow formed behind them and the cat pounced!

Millie Youngs (11)
Claines CE Primary School, Worcester

Ring! Ring!

"Today, we're going to do some maths," said Arthur Bear, the teacher.

"Woohoo, we love maths!" shouted the teddies. Dudgey wasn't paying attention as normal, he was pinching his twin sister, Fudgey.

"Ouch!" screamed Fudgey.

"What is it?" asked Arthur.

"Dudgey is pinching me!"

"Poorly Bear, would you mind sitting in-between them. Thank you. Well..." *Ring! Ring!* The fire bell went off. They all knew what to do. Sensibly, they all walked outside. Arthur called the names. Thankfully, they were all there, all eighty-two of them. It was only a practice. "Back into the class then," said Arthur Bear, relieved.

Ellie Roberts (11)
Claines CE Primary School, Worcester

Shoot For The Knees!

All the toys were wide awake while George's dreams were just beginning. "Attention!" Sergeant One bellowed.

"Here! Here!" echoed around. What was the mission about tonight?

"Out the window!" Where they were heading, no one knew.

"Sergeant!" Andy pleaded, "I'm stuck!" But he was gone, gone for the night.

"Incoming!" the sergeant cried. Who were they to battle tonight?

"Not the dog," Alfie groaned. Now his only fear, he had to battle.

"Shoot for the knees!" the sergeant called to him. Their rival fell to the ground. Returning to their boxes, the toys began to settle until the boy woke...

Tabatha Grinnell (11)
Claines CE Primary School, Worcester

Piggy's Adventure

"Are you ready Piggy?" said Pig.

"I'm ready," said Piggy. "Wait!" Piggy put on his jetpack. "Okay, I'm ready." Piggy stopped. He waited.

"Go!" shouted Pig. Piggy ran as fast as he could. He was nearly at the end now. "Jump!" Pig shouted. Piggy closed his eyes and jumped.

"Am I flying?" asked Piggy.

"No Piggy," said Pig sadly, "I told you it wouldn't work!

"Come on, let's try again, please!" pleaded Piggy.

"No, I've had enough of your silly games," Pig said. Piggy jumped off the edge of the windowsill and flew up into the warm air.

Seren Helena Jones (11)
Claines CE Primary School, Worcester

An Adventure Away From Home

After escaping from the bedroom, Eeyore and Arthur silently hid in a car, which was going to the beach.

At the beach, the teddies snuck out of the car. Wandering towards the sand, Eeyore asked Arthur, "What exciting thing shall we do?"

"Surfing?" Arthur replied.

"Race you to the sea!" Eeyore said excitedly.

In the sea, Eeyore asked Arthur, "Do you want a water fight?"

"Yeah! But what's the point? I'm gonna win anyway!"

"No, I'll win!" Eeyore said.

After their water fight, which they both claimed they'd won, the teddies went surfing on some waves even bigger than them!

Charlotte Roberts (11)

Claines CE Primary School, Worcester

The Battle Of The Bedroom

"Fire!" cried Colonel Green. *Bang!*
Bullseye muttered, "Sergeant Green?"
Meanwhile, underneath the floorboards, "Have we reached enemy lines?" moaned Private Beige.
"Shut up!" shouted Corporal Beige.
"I forgot the mine," said a nervous Private Beige.
"You useless buffoon!" boomed Corporal Beige.
"Where are they?" puffed Colonel Beige.
"They should be back up by now." Suddenly, loud thumps filled the air. The green toy soldiers looked on in horror.
"It's an action figure!" screamed a soldier.
"Help!" cried another.

Louis Delord (10)
Claines CE Primary School, Worcester

The Horses And The Girl

"Dinner time!"

"Okay Mum!" said the little girl. "Stay there horses, I'll be back."

One horse said, "I feel like I'm being tortured by this girl!"

"Same!" said the other horse. They stood as still as statues.

"I'm going!" said the brown horse, so he kicked the door open and went. Then the girl pushed open the door. The horse froze and hid. "That was close," whispered the horse.

"Where's one of my horses?" said the girl. The horse opened the door and walked out onto the landing. When he got through the door, he went onto the road...

Ellie Frost (11)

Claines CE Primary School, Worcester

Run And Jump!

Thump! My head hit the ground. A human-shaped figure loomed over me. Grinning maliciously, her fingers reached forward. "Lunch!" came a shrill voice from below me. Her mother. This was my chance. As she ran off, I seized the opportunity. "We can escape!" I called to the others.

"Quick!" came the voice of the sergeant. "We don't have much time, follow Soldier One." Crawling along the floor, we headed towards the windows. Taking a run and jump, Soldier One swung the window open. "Jump!" commanded the sergeant. One by one the toys jumped down, landing hard on the ground.

Freya Hooper (11)
Claines CE Primary School, Worcester

The Amazing Escape

One afternoon, Olivia's toys were waiting for her. They liked playing with her but they were bored. Mr Man was planning an escape. Mr Man ordered some items. "Catapult!" No toy hesitated, although they had no idea what was going on. As soon as he got it, he catapulted the toys into the garden. "To the tree," he said. They climbed the rope swing. Fortunately, they found a birdhouse. "Move in," he said.

Shortly after they'd settled, Olivia came, holding seeds. Once she'd spied them, she stared in fascination.

"They look nice there!" She skipped off. They were safe.

Sophie Williams (11)

Claines CE Primary School, Worcester

The Dangers Of Mount Laundry

The crooked terrain of Mount Laundry filled their view. A cluster of colours and an assortment of oddly-shaped clothing snaked up to the summit of the mythical mountains. The ambitious explorers' faces pictured both astonishment and terror. "Calm down," uttered the leader. "I know you're all raring to go but we need to lay down some ground rules." A sigh echoed around the room. Rules were more boring than triple maths! Tired of the captain's endless blabbering, an adventurous action figure crept towards the deformed heap of garments, oblivious of the dangers before him. He began his climb...

Noah Brownlow (11)
Claines CE Primary School, Worcester

The Day It Happened

I remembered the time it happened. The day I was forgotten about. It was a normal day until there was a bang. In the blink of an eye, the soldiers were in line. "What happened Sergeant?" I muttered. "Will we die?"

"No!" screamed Sergeant. "Don't be silly. Soldiers, look everywhere!"

Then I heard, "Matt's coming!" screamed a soldier. "And he isn't alone!" *Thump!* Something hit the bed. What was it? I heard music. Dancing music. I looked. It looked like a horse but with a horn. Was it? No way! A dancing unicorn! Why was it here? Why?

Bella Keates (10)
Claines CE Primary School, Worcester

Swago Taco Jr

"What was that?" There was a huge box in the corner of the room. There was a loud noise coming from it. "Troops, in position now!" Suddenly, a huge taco jumped out! His pages flicked rapidly and attacked Noah the telephone.

"Ouch!" screamed Noah. The troops were prepared for an attack.

A soldier shouted, "Hands up now!" He pointed the rifle at the taco.

"You wouldn't."

"Oh yes, I would!" It took him a second but he did. So the huge taco was limping back to his home - the horrid, cramped box. The huge taco was never seen again.

Joseph Laurence Mckay (11)
Claines CE Primary School, Worcester

Animal Adventure

"Good morning!" said Minnie Winnie with his cheerful voice.

"Ahh, go back to sleep!" shouted Flat Sheep.

Once Minnie Winnie was awake, there was no way he was getting back to sleep. All he had to do was wake his dad, Winnie the Pooh, and he would be in big trouble.

"Good m-morning!" sighed Blankie. For once, Magic the unicorn was the last one up. They heard a scream, they all looked around. Flat Sheep had fallen down the bunk bed stairs. Footsteps echoed around the house.

"The dog!" everybody screamed in unison.

"Run for your lives!"

Molly Siddles (11)
Claines CE Primary School, Worcester

The Great Toy Escape

At night, up in the top bedroom, under the bed, the toys were having a gathering. "Tonight is the night. This is our chance to escape," whispered Big Bear. "Why would we want to escape?" mumbled Fairy. "Because Lara never plays with us and we are tired of being trapped in this stinky, old cage."
When the toys had finished their discussion, they decided to crawl out from under the bed, keeping alert to make sure they didn't wake up Lara. They climbed up to the windowsill, each took a deep breath and one by one, jumped out.

Katie Frost (11)
Claines CE Primary School, Worcester

Legoland

There are many Lego kingdoms upstairs on 23 Stud Street, England. It goes from the undeniably cheesy kingdom of 'Friends', you have to be quadruple millionaires to buy all the cars, houses and cafes they own, to another world - Star Wars Kingdom. Has anybody else noticed Luke Skywalker probably could use his bushy hair as a mop? No one? Anyway, there's also the city's kingdom. I don't get why everyone's happy there, it looks crime-infested to me. I inherit the highest shelf. I tower over all the kingdoms, for I am the rarest of all. I am Mr Gold.

Joseph McRobert (11)
Claines CE Primary School, Worcester

The Stolen Puppy

"Help! Help me!" The angry pig, who stole the puppy, grabbed it and rushed off. He cackled away as his voice echoed in the distance. No one suspected a thing.
When it came for the puppy to be shown, the paparazzi crowded the curtains. *Bazam!* The curtains were opened and there was an empty space. Luckily, the puppy remembered that he had a camera on his collar. He cried and sobbed his little heart out. Suddenly, a voice was heard. "Puppy, bark if you can hear me!" The puppy barked. His agent knew what had happened and saved him.

Paige Frost (11)
Claines CE Primary School, Worcester

How To Not Escape A Room

"So, there's no one here. It's time," said the leader of the squad.

"Is it?" asked the member, Jack.

"Yes," replied James. They were a part of the gang. All members had to start with 'J', except for the leader because he had his own ways. Daniel, the leader of the team of Js, made music for them to listen to. The action figures didn't want to be in this 'dump' anymore. They were moving mobile figures and they were fast until the giant door opened and the giants, equally sized, stepped on them.

Theo Chevassut (10)
Claines CE Primary School, Worcester

Help!

"Help!" The red blaze engulfed me. My life flashed before my eyes. Chloe was gone. Stranded, in the middle of nowhere, alone to die. My plastic arms were merely victims to the heat. How did I get here, you ask? It was a beautiful day, Chloe took me out with her to the park. I loved our trips out together. This one, however, was not one of them! *Crash!* My vision disappeared.
When I finally awoke, the sun was nowhere to be seen. Slowly, I sat up. I was moving closer to an unfamiliar light. Red lights engulfed me...

Isabel Zara Toms (11)
Claines CE Primary School, Worcester

The Escape

"So Monkey, how are we going to get out?" wondered Sir Smile. They thought of a plan that might work. How would they manage to reach the window? That was the hardest part of the plan since it was five metres off the ground. They went on a hunt for rope.

Not long after getting into the cupboard, they found some rope. Once they had returned to the window, Monkey began to climb with the rope attached. Monkey was almost at the top, then the rope began to untangle. Luckily, Monkey managed to pull everyone up the rope.

Joshua Maiden (10)
Claines CE Primary School, Worcester

The Stealing Of Mord

Recruiting someone for the Pentagon was a secret organisation called Solemn, but as the Solemns were recruiting, they got hacked by none other than the Rodlikes. It was Rodlike 4932, the commander of all Rodlikes, with his bright yellow, gem-encrusted crown hair. Somehow, he stole Mord, the secret time-travelling machine. They picked Potlog, mostly as he had a sidekick called Ed Sheeran, to get Mord and bring it back and also, to kill Rodlike. Anyway, on they went to Paris, where Rodlike's HQ was.

Ben Kloos (10)
Claines CE Primary School, Worcester

The Unexpected Living Toys

The unexpected living toys had had enough of their horrible owner hitting and throwing them around. The toys were going to sneak out the window. One small toy jumped out and drowned in the mud. After his funeral, which was held in the cupboard, he was easily forgotten. Then, the toys broke out. As they walked down the road, a large, human-like figure loomed above them. Who was it? The human figure picked up the anxious toys. It was the owner! He was furious. What would he do with the toys now?

Mason Hadley-Chisam (11)
Claines CE Primary School, Worcester

The Runaway Teddy

The sun blinded me. Where was I? A huge hand reached into the inky-black darkness and picked me up. I found myself falling down. *Puff!* I was free. The park was an unusual place for a toy like me. *Woof! Woof!* I turned my head and a big husky stared right at me. I was frozen with fear. I ran. I ran as fast as I could. In the background, the voice echoed, "Penny, Penny, where are you?" My legs carried my sadness as I ran from her, my best friend, Lucy!

Katherine MacIntosh (10)
Claines CE Primary School, Worcester

Squished!

"The coast is clear!" said Rory.

"Ready your weapons," Captain Noddy whispered.

"On my command," Sergeant Scampi screamed, "charge!" The army figures ran for cover under the sofa and they mantled their weapons, but when they went to go somewhere else, a looming, immense figure came through the door and stepped on them. "Ouch!" Light covered the room in an instant. The figures had just been squished in one step!

Finlay Moseley (10)
Claines CE Primary School, Worcester

The Unicorn's Play Day

"The coast is clear," Bella said. The unicorns came out to play. They started to play tic-tac-toe. Bella went to play one of the new games. The game was called 'Don't Be A Donkey'. Minnie, Mimi and Bella came to play. It was a fun game. Every day, they played it again and again. All of a sudden, there was a squeak. Suddenly, they froze and a random inky-black shadow appeared out of nowhere...

Sophie Markham (11)
Claines CE Primary School, Worcester

Again!

"Seriously Pep, again? How many times have I told you we are stuck in this bag until she gets back!" grunted Fudge.

"But there must be a way out!" bounced Pepper excitedly.

"Well there isn't so get over it!" groaned Fudge.

"No!" squealed Pepper as she started digging her way through the tissue.

"Ugh! Why do I have to look after you?" moaned Fudge.

"Cheer up old bird!" laughed Pepper.

"I'm not a bird, I'm a dog..." Fudge was interrupted by an overexcited Pepper.

"I've found it, I've found the exit!" whispered Pep.

"What?" gasped Fudge in a gaze...

Miriam Jarratt (11)
Colwall CE Primary School, Colwall Green

The Toy Kidnapper!

One night in London, a shopkeeper closed the shop. All the toys were still, apart from two. The little toy princess, Brooke Carrington, wandered off the shelf. "Brooke, Your Majesty, what are you doing?" asked the toy soldier.

"The shopkeeper left the door unlocked. Ahh! Somebody's there, don't move," whispered Brooke.

"What a cute toy, I'll take you!"

Days later, Brooke woke up wondering where she was. "Where am I?"

"Brooke, where are you?"

"Archie, are you there? Help!" Archie went over, got her off the table, went downstairs to the front door to the shop and found a family.

Alice Stocking (11)
Colwall CE Primary School, Colwall Green

The Magic Dancer

Milly scanned the toyshop shelves in search of the perfect toy. Suddenly, she picked up a pink box with gold embroidery spiralling and twisting around the box, with blue tits fluttering around it. Wait, were they actually moving? No! Milly opened the box and listened to the music play and a pretty, dainty ballerina span around. Then, she started a much more complicated routine. Her arms wafted around beautifully. "That can't be mechanics, that's magic!" Milly gasped and closed the lid carefully, then ran over to her Mum. "Can I have this one?" The magic had begun once again...

Lucy Copeland (11)
Colwall CE Primary School, Colwall Green

Captured!

"Cola?"

"Yes?"

"I'm bored."

"Go and play." It was a cold winter's night and everything was silent. But all of a sudden, a customer walked their way into the shop. The customer saw Cola and grabbed him.

Ten weeks later, he escaped but he didn't know where he was! No one by his side, everything was dark and smelt damp. Suddenly, Cola tripped over something. He put his torch on and he realised he was home. It was the middle of the night but he still yelled, "Yippee!" Cola was finally home, then they had a massive party.

Emily Glover (11)

Colwall CE Primary School, Colwall Green

Wilbur The Old Piggy Bank

After many years of staring at the ornate oak mirror, there sat old Wilbur. For many moons, she had been forgotten, abandoned, neglected. Well, that was until a frail, tattered doll knelt down by her side, her dusty, bedraggled hair and chipped button eyes all reflecting into the glass. Years had flown since they were chucked into the musty attic. Wilbur was so old, she was leaking money! Gold and silver pieces slid to the floor. Glancing at Wilbur, the doll slowly reached her ripped arm over Wilbur's shoulder. A gentle friendship had formed between them, just from a mirror.

Emonie Huckle (10)
Colwall CE Primary School, Colwall Green

The Evil Doll Strikes

It all started in a cold, dark house where an evil doll lived. Her name was Lily D. Her owner was called Lily. Lily was scared of the doll that she got for her birthday. It was always moving. Lily called her mother, "Today Rowan is coming over for a sleepover!"

That night, they both went to bed very uncomfortably, thinking about Lily D.

Suddenly, they woke up and Lily D was there with Lily's kitten in her hands. Then *crash!* The girls threw Lily D off the bed and ran downstairs together. It had only just begun!

Tilly Amy Davies (11)
Colwall CE Primary School, Colwall Green

Grandma's House

As I pulled up at my grandma's house, the dread of playing boring Scrabble and having to go to bed early swam through my mind. I stepped out of the car, took a deep breath and knocked on her door. When she opened the door, a waft of her perfume hit me.

Later that evening, she showed me to my room for the night. I scanned the room but suddenly, my eyes stopped. I saw an old, crooked doll perched on a splintered shelf. Horrifyingly, it opened its eyes. Grandma and I stood in silence. "Ahhh!" The doll had gone...

Alysia Marriott (11)
Colwall CE Primary School, Colwall Green

The Everlasting Princess Toy

On a hot day, there was a wonderful princess that was brushing her hair. She went to her bedroom to find something to wear, she had a lot of clothes in her closet. Fiona went to the woods for a scavenger hunt, she found so many items, jewellery, phones, crowns and especially treasure! She went home, she was really tired.

When she got home, she had her tea, then she told her parents and siblings that she was tired and she went to her bedroom.

When she arrived, she decided to wear her PJs and get into her blankets.

Kombo Choma (11)
Colwall CE Primary School, Colwall Green

The Magical Lego Party

One night, Lucy was asleep. Her Lego Friends got up. Mia whispered, "Come on guys, let's have a party." Off they went to their bakery to get some cake and some balloons, then they set up the party and started.

In the morning, Lucy got up and saw the Lego Friends moving and having a party! Lucy joined in with the party.

After a bit, Lucy left them to have a party and went for a walk.

Later, Lucy found a fairy kingdom! A fairy was crying. Lucy took her home. She said, "I want a pet!"

Lucy Isherwood (11)
Colwall CE Primary School, Colwall Green

Red Rum

I was alone. I was the only doll to wake up. What had happened? I stepped out of my room and looked around the empty building. Where had everyone gone? I slowly walked forward to find glass on the floor. I looked up and saw a shattered window with blood dripping from the ceiling. What was going on? What had happened to my family? I turned towards the door and there it was. Writing. Writing above the door. I could barely read it but I could just make out that it said 'Red rum'. I realised that it meant murder...

Abi Knight (11)
Colwall CE Primary School, Colwall Green

Buddy The Cookie Stealer

It was dark in the lonely toyshop, aliens were breaking in. Security was coming, the aliens were blasting a cuddly toy monster with goo that could make it come to life! The aliens squeezed past the door. Buddy the cuddly toy monster jumped out of his box that he was put in. Security was coming. Buddy was running for his life! He knocked out the security man and put him in a locker.

A boy came the next morning and bought him but every night, Buddy would come to life and steal cookies, and the boy didn't know!

Ben Friedlander (11)

Colwall CE Primary School, Colwall Green

The Great

Joe is sat outside on a chair and really needs some water. Joe jumps up and runs into the kitchen. Someone walks past him, Joe is sweating at this point. He is hiding behind a chair. "Okay," he says to himself. Joe runs as fast as his little legs can carry him. He starts to climb. "Don't look down, don't look down!" Then he gets to the top of the sink. He turns on the tap but he falls in and sinks to the bottom. "Ahh, no!" He just stays there, alone.

Andy Smith (10)
Colwall CE Primary School, Colwall Green

Pink Diamond And The Gems

Sorrow from Lapis, crystal tears boomed from her eyes. She was in prison. She broke out of jail and she landed on Earth. She met friends. She loved her life. They were gems too. They protected their home and she learnt more every day.

One day, she met a strange girl. She started dancing, Sorrow started dancing as well. They became best friends. The girl was called Jasper but the gems defeated them and Jasper was destroyed. The years passed and the gems learnt a lot...

Rowan Clark (11)
Colwall CE Primary School, Colwall Green

Jazz And Ruby

Jazz, an eleven-year-old girl, lived with her mum in a small village. Her favourite toy, Ruby Rainbow, a unicorn, went everywhere with her.

On Monday, returning home from school, Jazz walked in on Mum destroying Ruby! Jazz screamed, "Stop!" Mum was shocked. Jazz took a big, deep sigh, tears rolling down her complexion, losing grip on Ruby.

The next morning, Jazz found Ruby in a cage. Ruby and Jazz could now be together all day. What adventures awaited?

Yvaine Ragen Fraser (11)
Colwall CE Primary School, Colwall Green

A Storm On A Kitchen Table!

"King Richard, we have found something called a time machine."

"King Richard, what does this do-"

"No!" But it was too late, he had just made him and this whole army disappear and now they had travelled back sixty-five million years. *Roar!*

"What was that?" A T-rex had appeared and an indosaurus, dilophosaurus and a pack of raptors. King Richard said, "Charge!"

The T-rex said, "Roar!" They were running towards each other but a sandstorm had encircled them. As the sandstorm disappeared, they found themselves in a heap on the kitchen table!

George Zavalis (9)

Dixie Grammar School, Market Bosworth

Snowflake's Toy Adventure

Snowflake was an adventurous bear with shimmering, aqua fur as soft as snow. Talking of snow, there was nothing she liked more. All day long, she played with her family.

One day, they decided to make a huge snowman. "We've finished!" shouted Snowflake's brothers. They went to bed that night, got up the next morning and found their snowman having an ice cold drink! Shocked but happy, the children played with him all day. The best thing was, it never stopped snowing where they lived so he didn't melt and stayed there for the rest of their long, happy lives!

Erin Brining (9)
Dixie Grammar School, Market Bosworth

Max's Cars Come To Life!

One snowy Saturday afternoon, a boy called Max was dreaming about being an F1 driver. He went upstairs to his playroom to play with his toy cars. Max lined the cars up, ready to race. RB13 was red, M06 was grey, SR18 was purple and FOF1 was pink. Just as Max was about to start the race, he couldn't believe his eyes! The cars started racing around the track by themselves! Max watched for hours in amazement. Suddenly, the door of the playroom opened and the cars stopped still in their tracks.

"It's time for tea," said Max's mum.

Cian Geaghty (10)
Dixie Grammar School, Market Bosworth

Teddy's Escape!

Teddy had always been John's most favourite toy, but that was all about to change...

One day, John went to the park with Teddy but when they got there, something tragic happened. Teddy fell into a thorn bush and one of his eyes fell off!

When John got home from the park that evening, he chucked Teddy in the bin. "Help! Anyone? What should I do? Shall I try and push the bin over?" Teddy pushed against the bin with all his might but it was no use. Suddenly, he heard footsteps getting louder. This was his only chance...

Issy Parkes (10)
Dixie Grammar School, Market Bosworth

The Magical Elf

One Christmas, a magical elf called Elfie was sent by Santa to watch over Imogen, to check she had been good. Elfie had loved Imogen for years and wanted to make an amazing entrance. Elfie decided to borrow Imogen's iPad whilst she was asleep and sneak into her room and take selfies with her, telling her how much he loved her.
When Imogen woke up in the morning and looked on her iPad, she saw the pictures Elfie took of her whilst she slept.
When it was time for Elfie to leave, Imogen was hoping he would return next year.

Imogen Green (9)
Dixie Grammar School, Market Bosworth

Barry And Steve Visit The King

Barry the robot and Steve the snake were toys who roamed the playroom, but there was one problem, the Lego people wouldn't play with them so they agreed to go and see the Lego king. They tried to get into the castle but all of their attempts failed so they dressed up as Lego guards and snuck in. They got past the guards and to the king. They asked the king if they could play with the Lego people. The king said, "Yes!" So the king shouted, "Everyone is allowed to play with the Lego people!" Everyone was happy.

Ioan Daniel Hust-Edwards (9)

Dixie Grammar School, Market Bosworth

Barry And The Soldiers

Once upon a time, there was a green toy soldier called Barry. Barry used to be in the special toy forces.

One day, he and his family were in the bedroom, searching for human evidence but the boy who lived in that room had just got back from summer camp. All of the little green soldiers screamed and then ran. Barry had no clue what was happening and kept looking for more human evidence. Barry's family screamed for him to come but he didn't. They left him! Barry heard loud stomping. He ran for dear life and escaped!

Oscar Harding (10)
Dixie Grammar School, Market Bosworth

Millie And Muffin

I am Millie, a magic bear. I can come to life. I play in the shop every night.

One night, I spotted a little dog. I stroked her and she came to life! "I'm Muffin," she barked. We became best friends. We had tea in the doll's house, we rode on bikes and we read books.

Until one day, a little girl came in looking for a birthday treat. She found Muffin and said to her mum, "I would love this little dog!" I watched her being paid for in horror. Would we ever find each other again?

Ava Constable (10)
Dixie Grammar School, Market Bosworth

Barbara The Barbie

Once upon a time, there was a cowboy. He wanted to fall in love with the girl across in the doll's house because they were toys. As they had only said hi to each other once, he walked over to her and she told him her name was Barbara the Barbie. She was running downstairs to walk the dog, her legs creaked as she ran around the park.

The cowboy was thinking about her all night, dreaming that one day, they might finally fall in love.

Skip five days and they fell in love and got married!

Felicity Ava Dracup (10)
Dixie Grammar School, Market Bosworth

Holly The Teddy Finds A New Friend

Holly woke up in her hammock and went outside to find a coconut for her breakfast. Suddenly, this other teddy called Ben came over but Holly didn't know why and then Ben said, "Do you want to be my friend?"

Holly said, "Yes, of course!" So Holly and Ben went outside in the jungle and suddenly, they heard a toucan. It was very loud, it looked like it was heading for them so Holly ran as fast as she could but it got her. The toucan didn't care about Ben. Holly shouted as loudly as she could, "Ouch!"

Amelia Grace Parker (9)
Fladbury CE (A) First School, Fladbury

The Save By Stardust

Once, Kasey, Koo-Koo, Pinkie, Zigzag and Penny were doing races up and down the bed. Suddenly, Kasey accidentally slipped off the edge. Koo-Koo tried to save her but slipped as well. The other toys tried to save them but fell. Luckily, Stardust was there. She dangled her tail down the bed for them to climb up. One at a time, they got back on the bed just in time because Elsie came in! Her school day was over. The toys kept that secret to themselves but they all knew the real truth and lived happily ever after.

Elsie Grace Morris (9)
Fladbury CE (A) First School, Fladbury

The Dream Turned Into A Rabbit And Cat

As tired as a hardworking teacher, Camilla, who was great at dreaming her brain out, dozed off to the land of the unknown. She entered into the clouds when a voice silently said, "Hello, my name is Diana and I am confined here until someone saves me from the witch who turned me from a human to a toy rabbit!" Camilla heard the rabbits cry and ran over to help.

"Greetings Diana, I heard your plea from miles away and decided to help."

"Okay!" said Diana. Whilst they were running, something extraordinary happened. Camilla was formed into a toy cat!

Zoe-Maria Palmer (11)
Harper Bell SDA School, Birmingham

Buffy And Pip

A cuddly lion named Buffy found a soft plushy in its enclosure. The curious lion walked cautiously towards it. "Stop, don't hurt me!" the mouse squeaked. The lion jumped back.

"What's your name?"

"Pip," replied the little toy mouse. Buffy smiled and cuddled with Pip. Buffy finally found a friend. Daylight appeared from the horizon. Buffy looked down at the floor. Pip had been stolen! Buffy broke out the enclosure and looked all over the zoo. Finally, he saw her in the garbage! He picked her up with his teeth and went back to his enclosure. They lived together.

Isobel Cole (11)
Hurley Primary School, Hurley

That Very Night

The young princess closed her eyes, not knowing what was going to happen that night. The Barbies trampled through the new toys to find a small unicorn. The sound of chatter filled the area. One Barbie suggested Truth or Dare? to play. The unicorn went first. She chose Clare. "I've got a good one for you! Wake up the princess!" Minutes later, a loud gasp filled the room. Everything stood still. Anxiously, the princess demanded to know who had woken her up. She looked around the room. "You!" It was the Barbies that got caught, not the unicorn!

Grace Thorpe (11)
Hurley Primary School, Hurley

It's A Winter Dream

On a winter's night, a boy named Sam went outside to play. He walked outside and played in the snow, he made the biggest snowman ever. He even had a snowball fight!

As he was going back inside, he noticed a green, glowing console. He walked over and closer until *bam!* He got sucked in! "Woah, what is this place?" He was inside Winter Wonderland! "Hello? Anyone here?" He was petrified! "How do I get out of here?" He was starting to panic. He ran around until he found a man, or that's what he thought...

Jack Samuel Freeman (11)
Hurley Primary School, Hurley

Toffee The Mysterious Bear

On a summer's morning in a small town called Lionville, there was a peculiar family. The mum and dad were both secret agents. They had a daughter called Anna, she was beautiful and loved toys. Her favourite was Toffee, he looked like his name. This year, they were going on a holiday. Anna chose to take Toffee.

A couple of days later, it was Anna's birthday. She was gifted a new bear by her parents. She soon forgot about Toffee and left him down the side of the bed.

That night, something very weird happened. Toffee came to life...

Jessica Jakovlevs (10)
Hurley Primary School, Hurley

The Bullied Toy Who Rose Up

There was a gang of despicable bullies. They were all tall and always picked on the tiniest toy.
His name was Kodla. He got bullied so bad that he ran away.
After three years, he came back. He had a terrible experience. The bullies picked on another kid, Kodla's best friend. He went bonkers! He was so mad, he wanted to fight but his best friend calmed him down. He said, "Why are you bullying us? If you tell us, we can help you." He owned up and told them everything. Would Kodla forgive the bully?

Josh Matthew King (10)
Hurley Primary School, Hurley

The Adventure

Meet Mr Cuddles. He was kind but simple. However, he was not loved by many toys and teddies but was his owner's favourite teddy. That night, he overheard his owner's parents saying that they were going away for the day tomorrow.

The next day when his owners left, he was off on his great adventures. First, he went down the River of Doom. That was just the beginning! All of a sudden, he was down. He jumped on the slippy, sliding ice. What a dreamer...

Hope Olivia Williams (11)
Hurley Primary School, Hurley

The Lonely Panda

It's hard being a toy panda. All the real pandas take the mickey out of me. I wish my dream would come true one day, to be a real panda.

Quickly, I woke up crying, then another toy panda, her name was Ruby, called for me every day.

Then one day, I quickly woke up and she wasn't there so I went to her house and I saw her dead on the floor! I got down on one knee and held her in my arm. A tear dropped from my eye, then she came to life...

George Knight (10)

Hurley Primary School, Hurley

Daredevils

Once, there was a toy named Copool. He was eating breakfast and there was a big bang. Copool got very scared. He ran outside, he started to get bigger. Copool got angry and walked up to his owner Reu. Reu promised to play with him and he started shrinking. Reu said, "I won't play with you until you say please."

"Fine!" said Copool. Copool said, "Please can you play with me Reu?"

Reu said, "Good boy Copool, for saying please."

"Can you play with me now?"

"I will play with you for one hour, good toy!"

Reuben Jenkins (9)
Kempsey Primary School, Kempsey

The Zom-Barbie Day To Nights

By day, she was a supermodel. At night, she was a zombie, which everyone scaredly ran away from. She was just a toy but she had been on the shelf for two years and she finally got bought. The owner of her was terrible. He had chopped her head off so she became the headless Zom-Barbie. Amanda Holden, the boy's little sister, found Zom-Barbie and fixed her. They both played tea parties and shops. Gradually, Zom-Barbie was changing to less zombie and more Barbie. The other toys weren't so scared anymore and they all played together, becoming very best friends.

Jess Popham (9)
Kempsey Primary School, Kempsey

Warrior Fight

In the forest, Rainbow was picking her berries like normal for her family. Rainbow was a warrior doll, her sister was a warrior too. Their parents were worried about when they started fighting each other and would get really hurt.

When Rainbow got home, Lillie her sister was dancing. Rainbow was the dancer, Lillie was the singer.

Rainbow went to the lake to relax when a crocodile started to fight her. Rainbow got out her sword and started to fight the crocodile. The crocodile ran to the village, Rainbow had saved the day!

Millie Harris (9)
Kempsey Primary School, Kempsey

Pinky Is Lonely

One day in a small room, a unicorn called Pinky was in her bed, thinking about her owner, Lily. She loved Lily but she never got to spend time with her so she wrote a letter: 'Dear Lily, I am upset because you never spend time with me and I am lonely. I need a friend. Your lonely friend, Pinky'. Lily thought and the next day, Pinky woke up with a fright. She heard a thud. Pinky ran downstairs and there was another unicorn called Spark! They played and played and Lily was happy.

Bethany Hoskins (9)
Kempsey Primary School, Kempsey

A Teddy Journey!

My name is Dragon and this is my journey. It was a normal day at the toy store and I said, "I'm going on a journey to find a family." So off I went on my journey. At first, I walked but then I got tired, then in front of me was a huge red thing. I jumped on a large black thing on a human's back. He was going on the huge red thing too.

After that, I jumped on a huge yellow thing. As I climbed on, I saw a tree. That was where my new family was!

Katie Cox (9)
Kempsey Primary School, Kempsey

Peaches My Toy Puppy

One day, Daisy, a little girl, decided to sort her toy box because it wouldn't close. She threw out all her toys. She found a glittery, fluffy dog called Peaches and it was her favourite toy but then she lost it. Daisy's mum was downstairs working, she ran downstairs and shouted, "Mum! Mum! Look what I've found! My favourite toy, Peaches! She was at the very bottom of my pink, sparkly toy box. Do you remember Peaches?"

"Yes, I do!"

"I found her just a minute ago. Do you like Peaches? I don't like Peaches, I *love* Peaches!"

Eloise Hardwick (9)
Kilsby CE Primary School, Kilsby

The Knight's Mission

In a faraway bedroom, Isla was playing. Her mum called, she left, switching the light off as she went. The king, queen and Joker in the castle feared the dark. The brave toy knight was lonely, the queen challenged him to rescue the princess from the dark palace. The knight found a secret corridor, where there stood a trusty steed that he rode to a locked cupboard full of books. He searched through every volume until, in the very last book, he found a key. Unlocking the door, he knelt to greet the princess and they fell in love!

Layla Rose (8)
Kilsby CE Primary School, Kilsby

The Forgotten Toys

Once, I was awesome, shiny and colourful as it should've been, until my owner's seventh birthday. That day, my owner got a new toy, it was an awesome Batman figure. I was just a teddy. From then on, I was forgotten and left under the bed. One night, I gave the new toy a piece of my mind but he wasn't bad. He wanted to help. The following morning the boy came into his room. He was going to university so put us in boxes and stored us in the cold, dark attic.
Not all stories are happy for toys.

Joshua David Hurwood Fuentes (8)
Kilsby CE Primary School, Kilsby

Dolly Polly And Her Escape From Home

Once upon a time, there was a family and they had a secret that they didn't know. Their toys came to life every night and if humans saw them alive at night, then they stayed a toy forever by not coming alive every night, like death. Polly the dolly one night got out the toy box and thought it was time to escape. She jumped out the window but forgot about the dog that nearly ate her! Polly managed to squeeze through a gap in the fence. She was free to explore the world and live happily forever.

Nicole Cloete (8)
Kilsby CE Primary School, Kilsby

The Toy Unicorn Who Wished To Fly

One day, a toy unicorn sat sadly in the corner of a little girl's room. The unicorn wished it could fly. It had tried running up the tunnel of a train track, lots of other things too. The unicorn thought about asking the little girl for help. He found the courage to ask her. Her idea was to tie fifteen balloons around his middle. He happily floated into the sky and waved the little girl goodbye. The little girl was sad to see him go but happy that he was happy.

Florence Stuart (7)
Kilsby CE Primary School, Kilsby

What's Happened To Me?

There was once a boy living in a small town. His name was Linky. One day, Linky woke up to feeling abnormal. "What's happened to me? I feel different," he said.

Five minutes later, "Darling, breakfast time!" his mum shouted.

After having breakfast, Linky stomped back to his room, feeling stressed. "Seriously, what's happened?" He was freaking out and panicked for five hours before he thought to ask his mum.

"Mum, I feel weird. Is anything wrong with me?" Linky asked.

"No sweetie," his mum replied.

After two more hours, he thought to look in his mirror. "I'm a toy!"

Diya Sharma (10)
Kingsway Community Primary School, Leamington Spa

The Toy Fashion Contest

In a nursery there lived many toys, Rainbow and Sparkle were unicorn soft toys. They were besties. "Attention! Attention!" the teddy yelled. Toys gathered up. "We're having a fashion contest on Monday. Anyone can participate. The winner will be classed as a diva toy." And he left. Everyone was jumping about. Sparkle dreamt of herself winning. Fortunately, she won! Rainbow broke friendships with her as she was annoyed. "Why'd you let a silly contest break your friendship?" everyone shouted. Rainbow soon realised and they were best friends again and never ever argued.

Rohini Patil (11)
Kingsway Community Primary School, Leamington Spa

Jack The Bunny's Golden Egg

One day, a boy bunny called Jack went into the forest with his mummy, Susie. He tripped over a rock which had a map sticking out of it. Jack showed his mummy the map. It was a treasure map. They decided to follow it. He spotted two magpies sat by a tree. Jack and his mummy knew magpies liked shiny things so they started digging when they heard a thud. "I've found a golden egg Mummy!" replied Jack. Running home, Jack showed Daddy. He was amazed!

He said, "I'm coming with you next time you go into the forest."

Jake Broome-Wright (9)
Kinlet CE Primary School, Bewdley

Jeff The Hero

Once upon a time, there was a bear called Jeff and one day, Jeff came alive, then he pushed a chair to his owner's backpack, then his owner got his backpack and walked out the front door and walked to school.
When he got to school, Jeff jumped out of the backpack and saved a little girl with ginger hair. Jeff got out of the bag, then pulled her top and dragged her off the windowsill, then Jeff jumped back into the backpack, then they both plodded home. Just then, some aliens appeared right in front of them...

Jack Waterhouse-Turner (10)
Kinlet CE Primary School, Bewdley

The Toy Comes To Life

One day, there lived a girl called Sophie. She lived with her mum and dad. She had so many toys that one day, her mum had given up on how many toys she had and threw them in the attic.

One rainy day, they heard a massive bang. It didn't sound like the rain at all so Sophie got her ladder and went up to the attic. She saw her favourite toy had come to life! She couldn't move. They loved playing together all day long but she couldn't tell anyone. It was a secret. She had a surprising day!

Katie Ann Dudley (9)

Kinlet CE Primary School, Bewdley

The Story About Buttercup

Once, there was a toy called Buttercup and she was a fairy. She had friends called Mya, Megan, Layla and her best friend was Layla. Buttercup said, "I really want something to drink but there's nothing!" But then she found a potion. After that, she started to grow. Buttercup said, "Ahhh!" She really didn't know what was happening. She made friends, she loved it.

One day, she found a boy and made friends with him.

Chloe Kinnersley (8)

Kinlet CE Primary School, Bewdley

Magical Sparkles Mystery

"Be quiet," whispered Sparkle. "The villain is peeking through the door."

"The ghost has vanished!" They peeked through the huge castle door and came out of their homes. Suddenly, the ghost returned to the bedroom, making scary, terrifying noises.

"You can't hide from me!" All the toys ran downstairs and ran into the kitchen and jumped into Lilly's dinner plate.

Meanwhile, the ghost continued following. Lilly nearly took a mouthful of her spaghetti. The toys managed to slide down the spaghetti ropes and hurried back to the bedroom. Eventually, Lilmy accidentally crushed the ghost. "Oops! They were only toys."

Sarah Ishraq Garnier (8)
Slade Primary School, Birmingham

Diamond Head's Heroic Act

Slade Village was a peaceful town, where Robert lived with his toy, Diamond Head. Everyone in the town was terrified when they found out that the village was ruined and no one knew. Robert said, "Where's my toy, Mum?"

Mother said, "What toy?"

"Diamond Head. I put it in my drawer but can't find it," Robert replied. Without their knowledge, Diamond Head came to life at night-time.

Diamond Head chased them and fought using his power to crystallise the bad toys.

In the morning, the villagers found crystallised toys along the road. From then on, the village became peaceful again.

Robert Neill Barachina Fortuno (7)

Slade Primary School, Birmingham

Seen

Hey! My name is Lloyd Garmadon. The son of Evil Lord Garmadon and I'm a toy. A Lego toy! My life is great. I have my friends, ninja friends, by my side all the time and today, my friends and I are playing.

It's an ordinary day. My owners are at school so we have the room to ourselves. It is great until... Just when I think nothing can go wrong, right at that moment, my owner just walks through the door and sees us! I am dead. I realise my friends have noticed. What will happen now?

Tanzeel Hussain (8)
Slade Primary School, Birmingham

Lost In A Game

After a long game, the young boy fell asleep. Gunshots filled the air. "Sergeant, what was that?" questioned one of the toy soldiers.
"Get the troops ready, get them into formation!" Together, the soldiers sought to find where the noise was coming from. On the floor was a board game, 'TANK'. Cautiously, in single file, they approached the game. Suddenly, a vortex opened, they were swallowed up. The soldiers had no idea if they would ever make it back to the bedroom. As the young boy awoke, he yelled to his mum, "Mum, have you moved my toy soldiers?"

Evan Rickard (9)
St Anthony's Catholic Primary School, Kingshurst

Fireworks!

It was Chinese New Year, the Year of the Dog, the festival celebration was in full swing. Everybody had filled the streets to party. A small child had brought along her dragon toy yet didn't realise she had dropped him in the excitement.
"Where am I? I do not recognise this street," murmured the dragon as he looked up into the crowds. Fireworks exploded painting the sky with vibrant colours. In fright, the dragon flew into the crowd and shrieked, "Where is my best friend?" At that moment, he remembered the words of the young girl to follow his heart.

Oliwia Hebel (11)
St Anthony's Catholic Primary School, Kingshurst

Amazing World Of Treats

There once lived a monster named Delicious. One fateful day, she ventured to a spectacular forest, Candy World. This place looked like Heaven, a world full of edible treats, she wanted to eat it all. As she entered, she quickly turned around to see a huge bunny staring back. Excitedly, she raced to begin to eat this huge feast. Suddenly, the stuffed bunny yelled, "You are trapped, you are now locked in forever!" Delicious began to tremble as the bunny began to turn into a terrifying beast. "It wasn't meant to turn out this way!" Delicious moaned.

Nariayah Webber (8)
St Anthony's Catholic Primary School, Kingshurst

The Unusual Bear And Family

In a small town, there lived a family. An unusual family. They were different from those in their town yet appeared to be normal. Yet it isn't about what is on the outside, it's what's inside that counts... right? The family had made much money because of teddies. These bears would soon change the entire world. Bears that appeared human, part of the family, had human abilities and emotions. A child's dream. What was unusual about the family? They were in fact robots. Human-like robots. But what did they do with the all the money? Who knows. Do you?

Angel Sandhu (10)

St Anthony's Catholic Primary School, Kingshurst

Toy Wars!

As Captain Tom (Leader of Toy Soldiers) led his team to the robot's encampment on the other side of the room, they were desperate not to wake the other toys. The plan was to steal the toy cannon, so they would become the coolest army in the bedroom. As they made their way to the opponent's base, suddenly a flashlight shone. The mum of the house had come to check that her son was sound asleep.

It was Mason's birthday the following day, mum had finished wrapping his presents. Suddenly, the whirring of the robots could be heard!

Keontai Nathan Miley-Morgan (9)

St Anthony's Catholic Primary School, Kingshurst

Unicorns Crusade

Isla, a young girl, had so many toys she really didn't know what to do with them.

As she woke one early morning, from out of her window, she spotted a toy sale.

Isla was eager to add to her collection. She pleaded with her parents to take her to buy yet another plaything. Eagerly, she slipped on her shoes and raced out the door to the first stall. Sat on the shelf, staring at Isla, was Unibat.

Finally, Isla's parents caught up with her in time to purchase the newly-loved thing. What adventures would the pair encounter?

Brooke Sims (9)

St Anthony's Catholic Primary School, Kingshurst

Phillipe, The Moving Mobile Phone

Leaving her phone on charge in her bedroom, the young girl was completely unaware that her new mobile phone could talk as well as walk.

Later, she checked that her phone had charged but to her surprise, it was now on the side of the room. In astonishment, she watched on as the phone began to move as well as talk. "Mum, help me!" she screeched. Taking a stick from the garden, the young girl began to smash the phone into pieces. Now, Phillipe the moving mobile phone was merely a pile of shards of glass and metal.

Darion Deathridge (10)

St Anthony's Catholic Primary School, Kingshurst

Pigs Vs Ponies!

There was once a girl called Mabel who owned lots of toys. In her bedroom, there were three shelves and on the top one, there were all her favourite toys, including her special piggy bank full of pennies.

One day, three of Mabel's ponies climbed up to the piggy bank and tried to take its coins. The pig bent over and shot each pony with pennies, causing the three of them to fall off the shelf and back into their box on the floor, just in time because Mabel entered the room. "Why are there coins everywhere?" she asked herself.

Alice Worley (11)

St Barnabas CE First & Middle School, Drakes Broughton

Casey's Snowy Adventure

Hi, I'm Casey and I'm a koala teddy. It's snowing outside and it looks great fun. Hmm, what do to? Aha! I'll inspect the snow from the window. Oh, how marvellous! It's so clean, white and crisp. I'd love to reach out and touch it. Ahh! I've fallen out! What am I to do now? Wait. What's that noise? Oh, a squirrel and he's pointing to a ladder on the drainpipe. It's my way home! So I climb it and aha! Here's my owner's room. She's seen me and is picking me up for a hug. I love her!

Beatrice Emilia Burrows (11)
St Barnabas CE First & Middle School, Drakes Broughton

The Toys On Strike

Jeremy opened his rusty, ancient toy chest to discover a mysterious letter. It read: 'Dear Jeremy, I will warn you now, this is not a positive letter. Us toys are on strike and have ditched our box (on a long holiday to India). This is what we have to say.' 'Jeremy, this is a stern note from Tony Tractor. Ever since you saw me at Smyths Toys Superstores, you wanted me. The 8th birthday you received me, you put me to the side and ignored me. You only played with me once and I'm totally sick of it!'

Madison Amelia Tustin (11)

St Barnabas CE First & Middle School, Drakes Broughton

What Is That?

Ted, Sam and Bob went to the big object in front of the toy box. It moved when Bob tapped it and sang a song. "Argh!" screeched Ted while he jumped backwards.

Sam was listening to the object when it sang, "Wind the bobbin up, wind the bobbin up, pull, pull, clap, clap, clap!"

"Huh?" Sam exclaimed excitedly.

"I don't know what that is," said Ted. They all stood around it, confused.

Then Bob said, "Why don't we name it?"

"Sure, why not?" answered Sam.

Ted said, "Why don't we call it a jack-in-the-box?" They all agreed.

Olivia Edwards (11)
St Bede's Catholic Middle School, Redditch

Twilight And Isabel To The Rescue!

Ding, the clock struck midnight. "It's safe to go," whispered Isabel.

"Rescue on the way!" exclaimed Twilight. Isabel and Twilight were best friends. Twilight was a soft, fluffy, toy unicorn and Isabel was her human girl. *Poof!* Twilight and Isabel were at Sparkle Mansion - all they could hear were screaming sounds.

"It's the bandits!" they whispered. They snuck in. Twilight kicked them with her hooves and they were out! The Lego police came and arrested the bandits. The little girl thanked them. *Poof!* They were back lying in bed, Twilight and Isabel were big again and soon fell asleep.

Georgia Keyte (10)

The Croft Preparatory School, Stratford-Upon-Avon

My Helping Hand

"Mum, what time is the rugby tomorrow?" said Ollie.

"I've told you already, you haven't cleared your bedroom up so you cannot go to rugby. Go to bed now!" Mum said angrily. Ollie marched upstairs in shame, shaking his head solemnly. He thought about captaining his first match but he had blown it.

In the dead of night, Nuts and Bolts, the mechanical robots, came into action. "Come on Nuts, let's help this poor lad." Nuts and Bolts marched downstairs and into the playroom. They started to clear it, this was a miracle! Maybe Ollie would be captain after all!

Charlie Feaver (9)

The Croft Preparatory School, Stratford-Upon-Avon

The Demon Conveyor Slide

Clunkety Clunk went the broken toy soldier as it toppled down the conveyor slide. Fred was the next in the queue to go down the conveyor slide, with all his friends behind him. It wasn't looking good for Fred and his friends. Just after they heard the toy soldier hit the bottom all battered up, Fred had an idea. "Why don't we join hands so that the man can't put us down the conveyor?"

"That's an excellent idea, let's do it!" agreed Tommy. Along came the man, he tugged at Fred but couldn't free him. The toys had done it!

Tim (10)
The Croft Preparatory School, Stratford-Upon-Avon

The Ghost Of Raffy

Clip-clop, clip-clop! Raffy was out of bed, heading for the basement. *Bang!* The door to the basement closed. Raffy was locked in! He banged the wooden door, hoping it would open. His owners heard, thinking it was a ghost. Raffy eventually fell asleep. His owner Nathaniel and his dad came down in the middle of the night. His dad, holding a red crowbar, opened the locked basement door. There in the centre of the room was Raffy, fast asleep. Nathaniel took him back upstairs and tucked him in. Raffy's adventure was over, or that's what they thought!

Nathaniel Joshi (10)
The Croft Preparatory School, Stratford-Upon-Avon

Not Your Average Princess

Princess Susie stood in her box in the big toyshop, in the middle of a huge row of identical Princess Susie dolls. She frowned at the silly nattering of the other Susie dolls, commenting on each other's lovely, sparkly shoes and silky hair. *I wish I was a superhero,* she thought to herself, *or an Action Man. Anything, rather than sitting around doing nothing, looking pretty. I wish I came with a motorbike, not a soppy pony.* Then, a girl wearing dirty dungarees and carrying a skateboard picked her box. *Things might not be so bad after all...*

Theo Holland (9)
The Croft Preparatory School, Stratford-Upon-Avon

Lego Mayhem

Bang! The toy store doors shut for the night. "Race on!" Four Lego mini figures opened their yellow packets. They jumped from the stacked boxes on the shelves and ran down to the toy cars in the next aisle. Two in a box, they ripped them open and the cars fell to the floor. Two mini figures rolled the cars into position and the others, Jim and Jeff, got into the cars. "Go!" They zoomed along the aisle. Jeff crossed the line first. There was a big cheer from the dolls. Suddenly, the doors opened. "Quickly, back into your bags!"

Daniel Nichols (10)
The Croft Preparatory School, Stratford-Upon-Avon

Mr Stuffy And The Lucky Child

One dark and stormy day at Toys 'R' Us, there was a new toy called Mr Stuffy. Mr Stuffy was hilarious but at that moment, he had no friends to laugh with.

The next day, Mr Stuffy found out a way to escape. He had to get rope, scissors and more importantly, himself. Once he had found how to use the tools, he started. He found a very beautiful house, just on the outskirts of Pebworth.

When he got to the house, he scanned the house with his lasers and found the room he needed. The lucky girl's beautiful bedroom...

Georgia Eve Hay (10)

The Croft Preparatory School, Stratford-Upon-Avon

Felix's Christmas

I am Felix. One week ago it was Christmas Day. In the morning, I opened one of my presents and inside was a monkey teddy bear. I named it Banana.

The next day, I was at school. I brought Banana to show my best friend, Oscar. But when I opened my bag to take him out, I couldn't find him. I searched everywhere but I still couldn't find him.

The next day, I spoke to my teacher about it. She recommended the lost property box. I hadn't thought of that!

When I got there, something was sticking out. Guess what?

Alannah Swift (10)
The Croft Preparatory School, Stratford-Upon-Avon

The Robotania War

It was a cold, rainy and foggy day. Once more, Simon, the leader of the dog army and Jeffery, the leader of the cat army were up to no good! They were fighting again in the Robotania freedom field. "Attack!" screamed Simon, they were off again! The dogs ploughed their way through the cats' defences and managed to get to the cats' base - Cat HQ. The dogs knew that if they got the cat control, the cats would turn good again. They had to do it! They got the control and turned the cats good. The dogs ruled again.

Benji Thorne (10)
The Croft Preparatory School, Stratford-Upon-Avon

The Charity Shop

Emily was with her friend, Ellie. They were both trapped in a dark and gloomy cardboard box when suddenly, there was light! A small hand appeared from the mysterious light and picked up one of the two friends. The box closed and all that was left was the remains of the two friends. It took an hour to find out where she had been taken. Emily was at the charity shop, waiting to be sold to a new owner but Emily wasn't thinking about the future. She was thinking about her friend Ellie and when she would return...

Olivia Phillis (10)
The Croft Preparatory School, Stratford-Upon-Avon

The Sad Bunny

One sunny morning, my family and I went on an outing in the car and I took my special bunny, Silky. On the way, my annoying little brother let the windows down and threw Silky out of the window because the wind was so strong. Then he landed in a stinky, slimy dustbin and it was ages until we found him. When we did find him, Mum insisted that he should go to the charity shop because he was so tatty.

Hopefully, someone nice bought him and he got a nice home, but I would never forget about Silky.

Beatrix Burman (10)
The Croft Preparatory School, Stratford-Upon-Avon

A Bat's Life

I had just finished a long section of my life. I was a cricket bat and had helped a young scholar to play cricket. When he started, he needed lots of help but as he grew older, he didn't need me to assist him. It began when he bought me for Christmas. I came to his house and he tried me out. He did well with my help, his score - a century! As all happy things did, our relationship ended at the end of his career, but he passed me on to his son, who was even better!

Thomas Russell (10)
The Croft Preparatory School, Stratford-Upon-Avon

The War Between Blue And Green

"Commander, we are under assault!" shouted Trooper 12.
"Okay, battle positions!" said Commander John.
"Yes sir!" shouted Squeak.
"Move up!" said Trooper 102.
"Fall back!" said Blue Trooper.
"Yay!" Trooper 12 said joyfully.
The next day. "Okay men, train!" shouted Commander John.
"Yes sir!" said Squeak.
"So Trooper 102, do you know how old John is?" said Trooper 12.
"No but he was made in the year 1910," said Trooper 102.
"Wow!" Trooper 12 said surprisingly.
"All meet outside please!"
"John, why is it blue here?" said Trooper 12.
"Oh, we are just going!" said Commander John.

Daniel James Beaman (9)
The Willows CE Primary School, Stratford-Upon-Avon

The Picnic

"Can I join the picnic?" asked Sparkle.
"Sorry but there's not enough food," replied Molly.
Sparkle was upset so he went and hid inside.
Billy whispered, "Good, he's gone."
Back inside, Sparkle could hear noises coming from the stairs. It was Fluffy, Sparkle's best friend.
"What's wrong?" Fluffy questioned.
"They won't let me join the picnic," Sparkle whimpered, then Fluffy had an amazing idea.
"How about we have our own picnic?"
Sparkle replied, "Yes!" They played games and had lots of fun.
The other toys saw the picnic and asked, "Can we join?" Sparkle nodded. Everybody had lots of fun.

Isabella Mae Charles (8)
The Willows CE Primary School, Stratford-Upon-Avon

The Harmless Dog

Pink the pig and his friends were having a picnic. "Oh, what a delicious sandwich!" announced Freddie the fox. In the distance, they could see a shadow looming over them. It was Timmy the dog. "Can I join your tea party?" asked Timmy.

"Picnic," corrected Freddie.

"You're just going to wreck it," exclaimed Pink the pig.

"Come on, I am just going to have a cup of tea."

"Retreat!" shouted Freya Frog.

"Us posh toys can't be seen with a messy dog having a 'tea party'!" bellowed Pink.

"Picnic," corrected Freddie. Timmy started sobbing. "I just wanted a friendly picnic!"

Ava Craddock (9)
The Willows CE Primary School, Stratford-Upon-Avon

Argument Then Friends

"It's a sunny day again," exclaimed Bunny.
The other toys moaned, "No it's not, it's raining."
Bunny knew they were lying because she could see.
"No, you're just lying!" Bunny moaned.
"No, it was raining and it's still raining now," complained the others. Bunny really wanted to shout but she knew Maisie would hear.
"Ssh, listen," whispered Bunny. She could hear Maisie playing with something.
"I can't hear anything," insisted one toy, then the toy opened.
"Freeze!" Bunny demanded, then Maisie came in with a new toy! It was a cat toy. Bunny had made a good friend at last!

Hannah Gascoyne-Davies (8)
The Willows CE Primary School, Stratford-Upon-Avon

The Attack

It was World War Two and a squadron of Spitfires was about to take on a mighty group of Lancaster bombers. They took off in seconds! It was going to be a fight to the death! Suddenly, Top Soldier radioed to the air chief marshal. "Look, we are outnumbered. We need to retreat, and fast!" The Lancaster bombers started dropping bombs.

"Chief, we need to save Dogton!"

"Eh?" replied the air chief marshal.

"Quick, retreat!" Suddenly, something walked into the room.

"Freeze!" shouted Soldier One.

"What's happened?" Jack asked himself. "Probably nothing."

Alfie Price (9)

The Willows CE Primary School, Stratford-Upon-Avon

The Escape!

"We're out of the box!" Squishy Number One whispered.

"We need a plan," said Squishy Number Two.

"I've got it!" said Squishy Number One. "Squishy number three, get that slime and stretch it out."

"Yes, boss."

Meanwhile, Squishies One and Two opened the window. "Done," whispered Squishy Number Three. "Now I'll dangle the slime from the window and you two climb down, then I'll jump," said Squishy Number One.

The next morning, no one noticed the squishies had disappeared. The squishies were very happy and were never sad again.

Francesca Bannister (9)

The Willows CE Primary School, Stratford-Upon-Avon

The Haunted Doll's House

John was under the big bed. He was playing chess with his tiger friend, Tigie.

At night, they were walking by a haunted house. John said, "Shall we look inside?"

"Yes," said Tigie. They looked inside. *Boo, boo, boo,* went a noise. *Boo, boo,* it went again. Tigie and John were terrified but they went inside anyway.

"Let's go upstairs." They went up the stairs until they reached gigantic doors. The door opened. Inside was a big ghost but it wasn't terrifying at all, it just wanted friends. They all made friends and played happily together.

Wiktor Czeszejko (9)

The Willows CE Primary School, Stratford-Upon-Avon

The Mistake

"Formation soldiers. The spy squadron has been arrested, the other platoon has died."
"Code red!" shouted the scout.
"Formation soldiers!" demanded the sergeant again. They stood in the middle of the floor and waited and waited and waited.
"This is boring," whispered the scout. Suddenly, a pistol shot went off. All the soldiers headed back to base.
"We need to find the crown jewels!" demanded the sergeant.
"Code red!" From out of nowhere, the enemy appeared with heavy, suppressive fire. The whole army died...

Matthew Hemming (8)
The Willows CE Primary School, Stratford-Upon-Avon

The Secret Life Of Squishies

One night-time, a girl called Sophie fell asleep, then out from nowhere, some of her squishies jumped from Sophie's bag and started to plan something, and do you want to know what it was? "Right, we're planning to escape," whispered Pig. "Right. Wait. Some of us don't have legs," Chick whispered. Suddenly, Bear had an idea and it was to build a giant car. So they did, then they drove off.

Minutes after, Sophie woke up and was about to squish a squishy and suddenly noticed that they were gone!

"No!" she cried and fell asleep.

Sophie Olivia Hall (9)
The Willows CE Primary School, Stratford-Upon-Avon

Model Search

Have you ever wondered what happens in your bedroom when you're not there to see it? Well, that is what this story is about! If you're intrigued, read on...
"Sculpting time! Line up in an orderly fashion please models. Sculpt into something beautiful!" bellowed Grand Claydon. He then walked along the line of models. There were models of flowers and a selection of macaws. When Grand Claydon got to the end of the line, he stopped. "Missing model!" he screeched, they went off to find it. They searched and searched until they found a brown dot on the floor!

Isaac Barnes (9)
The Willows CE Primary School, Stratford-Upon-Avon

Toy Argument

Have you ever wondered what it's like to be a toy?
Why might you ask? Well, this is a story about toys.
The thing about toys is that some of them can
come to life!

"You're not going to school with him, I am," said
Snowy.

"But he chose me, I'm the best!"

"Frankie, that isn't true," said Euan, who was a boy
that could talk to toys.

"But you said I could come with you!"

"Because my teacher said I could bring a toy to
school. Come now Frankie, go and get ready. It's
time for fun at school!"

Euan Clarke (8)

The Willows CE Primary School, Stratford-Upon-Avon

Rebel Ruby

When I came home from school, I noticed that my favourite doll, Ruby, had moved. "Hmm, that's not where I put you!" I picked Ruby up and put her on my bed and went downstairs.

Back upstairs, Ruby had moved again. "Hello, Cori." I stood still in my room, shocked. Ruby stood up and threw all my toys off my bed.

"What are you doing Ruby?" I shouted. Ruby laughed evilly, then she rubbed slime all over my pillow.

"I am Rebel Ruby, the meanest doll alive!" And then she ran out of the house.

"No! Bye Ruby!"

Cori-Annabel Tonia Byron (9)
The Willows CE Primary School, Stratford-Upon-Avon

Out On The Road

Mr Car Transporter was driving along the road when he heard a loud crash. He looked out of the window and saw the taxis had crashed into each other. He used his crane to pull the taxis apart, then he attached a rope and towed both taxis to the local garage. He called the police and at the garage, they searched the taxis for alcohol to see if that was the reason for the crash. They found six bottles of alcohol. The taxis were drunk. Luckily they survived but were taken to jail and they were banned from alcohol forever.

Michael Green (9)
The Willows CE Primary School, Stratford-Upon-Avon

The Battle Over Friendship

One misty night, Oli jumped into bed and fell asleep. Lego Character One woke up and said, "Wake up guys, we need to escape. Quick, get your things. Here comes Evil Master on a plane, get ready to attack!"

"He's turning around, he doesn't want to fight!"

"Right, I'm going to feed the pigs. Where are they?"

Evil Master came and explained, "I stole your pigs because they always die when they are with you! Can we be friends?"

"Yes."

Oliver Hill (8)

The Willows CE Primary School, Stratford-Upon-Avon

The Magic Unicorn

A girl is watching TV and falls asleep and then her unicorn comes to life. She goes downstairs and gets some food and then goes to her friend's house. They have a midnight feast. They have a party and eat popcorn, then they start making unicorn cupcakes. The unicorn starts mixing the batter until it is smooth. She puts it in the oven. They are finally done and they are golden on the top. She mixes the frosting and puts it on the cake. She has a drink, then goes back to bed, where she sees Lily.

Lily West (9)
The Willows CE Primary School, Stratford-Upon-Avon

Toy Story Of Terror

One night when the toys were watching a movie in the car, suddenly, they went over a bump and Sheep fell into a box. She was scared. They tried and tried and finally, got her out.

Finally, they arrived at the hotel. They went to their room. Their owner fell asleep so they wriggled out of the bag. Sheep was gone! Everybody was lined up. They found a hole she could have gone down. Then they were all pushed down.

When they got down, they all went missing. The man was selling kids' toys!

James Hales (9)
The Willows CE Primary School, Stratford-Upon-Avon

Est.1991

YOUNG WRITERS INFORMATION

We hope you have enjoyed reading this book – and that you will continue to in the coming years.

If you're a young writer who enjoys reading and creative writing, or the parent of an enthusiastic poet or story writer, do visit our website **www.youngwriters.co.uk**. Here you will find free competitions, workshops and games, as well as recommended reads, a poetry glossary and our blog.

If you would like to order further copies of this book, or any of our other titles, then please give us a call or visit **www.youngwriters.co.uk**.

Young Writers
Remus House
Coltsfoot Drive
Peterborough
PE2 9BF
(01733) 890066 / 898110
info@youngwriters.co.uk

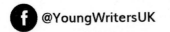 @YoungWritersUK   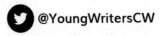 @YoungWritersCW